Roundabouts
by Eileen Diamond

21 new Rounds with Optional Instrumental Accompaniment

The majority of rounds available today date back many years, even centuries in origin. Although they are still enjoyable and fun to sing, this is a new collection of modern rounds for today's school children to sing and enjoy, and pass on anew.

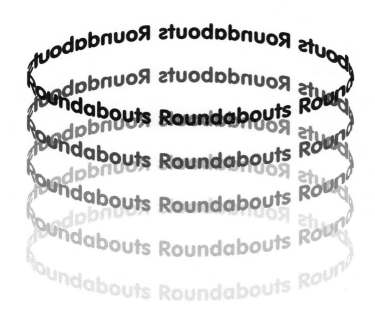

First published 1983
This edition published 1993
© **International Music Publications Limited**
Southend Road, Woodford Green, Essex IG8 8HN, England.

215-2-52

Teacher's Notes

Instrumentation

The instrumentation used in ROUNDABOUTS is only a suggestion, and may be varied according to which instruments are available at the time. Although melody instruments are not used in these arrangements, there is no reason why recorders, strings and other 'C' instruments should not be included. If a selection of several rounds are performed in concert, vary the instrumentation.

Accompaniment Ostinatos

Where alternatives are not given, each ostinato may also be used as an introduction and coda to the round. (An introduction is of course necessary for the performers to 'find their notes'. If the round is being performed unaccompanied, a single note will need to be given.) The rounds may also be sung unaccompanied or with any of the instrumental or voice parts omitted.

The possibility of variety in performing the rounds is enormous. Roundabouts, the first round in the book may, for example, be performed as follows:

Introduction

1. PIANO plays ostinato (twice)
2. The VOICES join in (ostinato twice more)
3. The PERCUSSION joins in, and the ostinato continues into the . . .

Round

4. CHOIR sings round once in unison
5. CHOIR sings round three times in parts

Coda

6. Ostinato once through
7. Ostinato 'last time' bars

This will make a piece of about $1\frac{1}{2}$ minutes.

Learning a Round

Each round must first be learnt in unison before part singing is attempted. Four part rounds may be sung first in two, and then three parts, until the performers are confident enough for all four. Similarly, sing three part rounds in two parts first.

Remember, before starting, to decide how many times through the round is to be performed!

NOTE:

In Don't Forget Me and The Seasons Round, the piano accompaniments have been written out in full to accommodate the irregular harmonic progressions.

Roundabouts

TWO PART ROUNDS

THREE PART ROUNDS

FOUR PART ROUNDS

TWO PART ROUNDS
ROUNDABOUTS

Words and Music by EILEEN DIAMOND

Driv - ing a - round on a round - a - bout go - ing round and round and round. Don't drive too fast or the ex - it you'll pass and you'll keep go - ing round and round.

ACCOMPANIMENT OSTINATO

Round and round and round and round. Round and round and round.——

SINGING AROUND (2 parts)

Words and Music by EILEEN DIAMOND

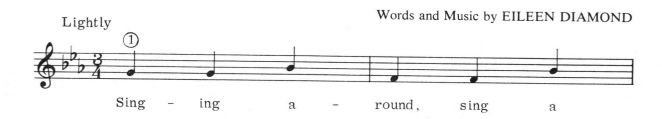

Sing - ing a - round, sing a round, If you're the one to start be sure to keep your part, When you're sing - ing a round. Oh!

ACCOMPANIMENT OSTINATO

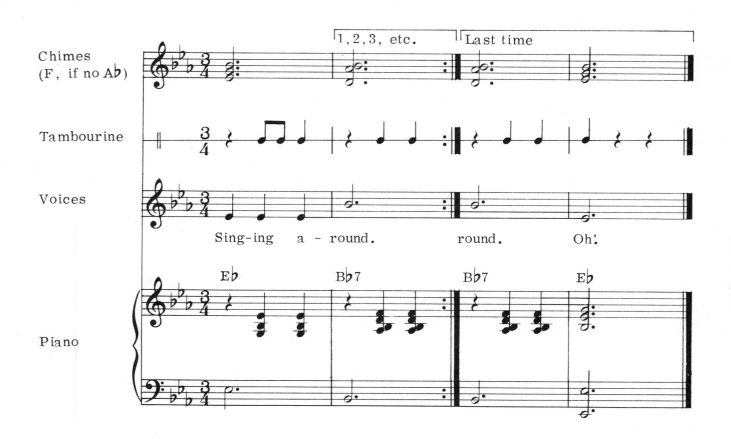

Sing-ing a - round. round. Oh!

WHAT IS THE WEATHER DOING TODAY? (2 parts)

Words and Music by EILEEN DIAMOND

Not too fast

*What is the wea - ther do - ing to - day? The
sun is shin - ing. Will it keep on shin - ing or
will it go a - way? You'll have to wait and see.

ACCOMPANIMENT OSTINATO

*Alternative verses:

The rain is pouring. (Will it keep on pouring?)
The wind is blowing. (Will it keep on blowing?)
It's cold and snowing. (Will it keep on snowing?)
It's dull and cloudy. (Will it stay all cloudy?)

*Children may also like to make up their own verses.

DON'T FORGET ME (2 parts)

Brightly – with humour

Words and Music by ELEEN DIAMOND

Don't for-get me when you go a – way, Please re-mem-ber me from day to day, Out of sight is out of mind, Then an-oth-er is not hard to find.

ACCOMPANIMENT

AUTUMN (2 parts)

Words and Music by EILEEN DIAMOND

ACCOMPANIMENT OSTINATO

LAZIN' IN THE SUMMER SUN (2 parts)

Leisurely

Words and Music by EILEEN DIAMOND

Laz - in' in the Sum-mer sun—— got no work to do,

Bet - ter sing this song a-gain —— all the way through.

ACCOMPANIMENT OSTINATO

Laz - in' Sum-mer—— sun, We're just a -
(Last time: sun.)

THE SEASONS (2 parts)

Words and Music by EILEEN DIAMOND

Win - ter is o - ver at last at last.

Spring - time is here.——— Sum - mer is com - ing, and

Aut - umn will fol - low, And there goes an - oth - er year.

ACCOMPANIMENT

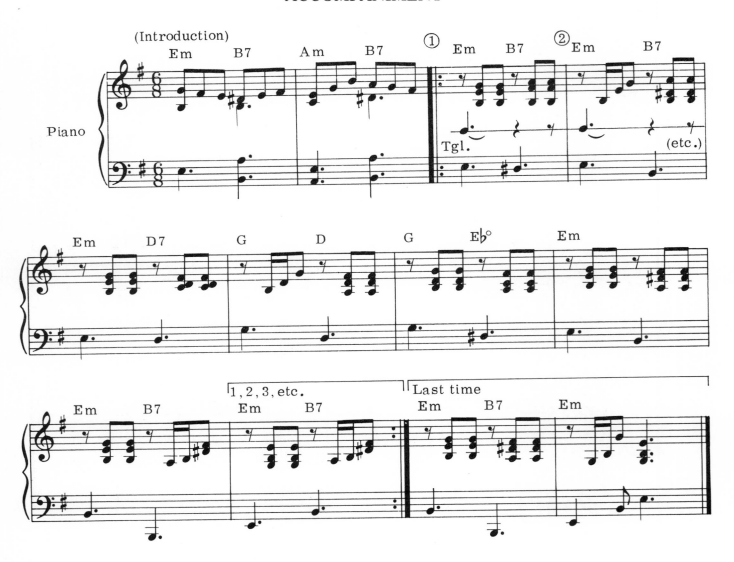

CHRISTMAS (2 parts)

Cheerfully

Words and Music by EILEEN DIAMOND

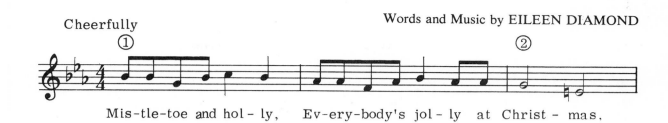

Mis-tle-toe and hol-ly, Ev-ery-body's jol-ly at Christ-mas,

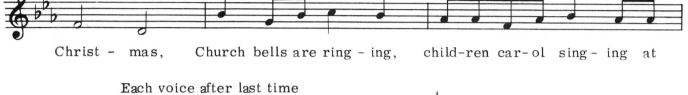

Christ-mas, Church bells are ring-ing, child-ren car-ol sing-ing at

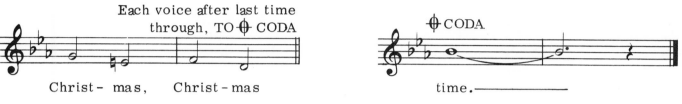

Each voice after last time
through, TO ⊕ CODA

⊕ CODA

Christ-mas, Christ-mas

time.———

ACCOMPANIMENT OSTINATO

THREE PART ROUNDS
LET IN THE SPRING

Words and Music by EILEEN DIAMOND

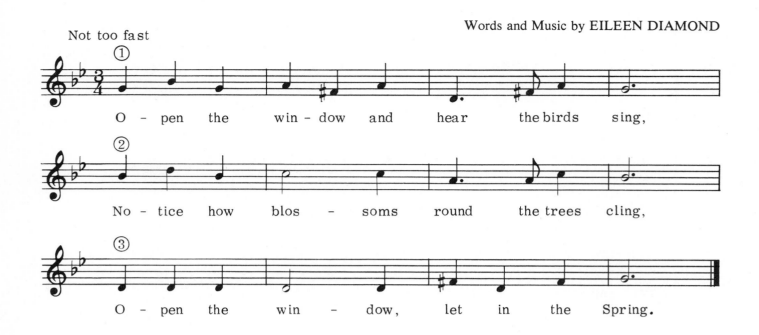

ACCOMPANIMENT OSTINATO

THE BIRTHDAY ROUND (3 parts)

Words and Music by EILEEN DIAMOND

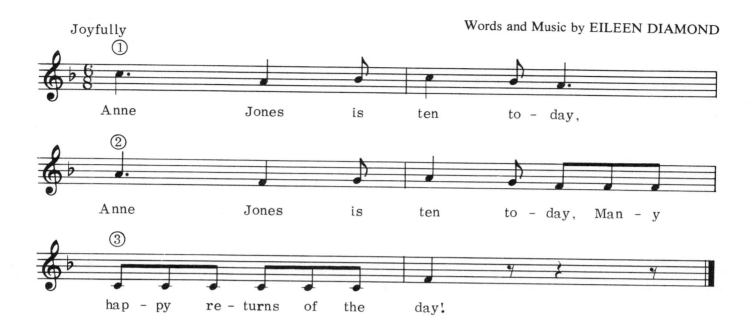

ACCOMPANIMENT OSTINATO

NOTE: Change the rhythm where necessary to fit various names and ages.
(It may sometimes be necessary to use an up-beat).

SAILING (3 parts)

Words and Music by EILEEN DIAMOND

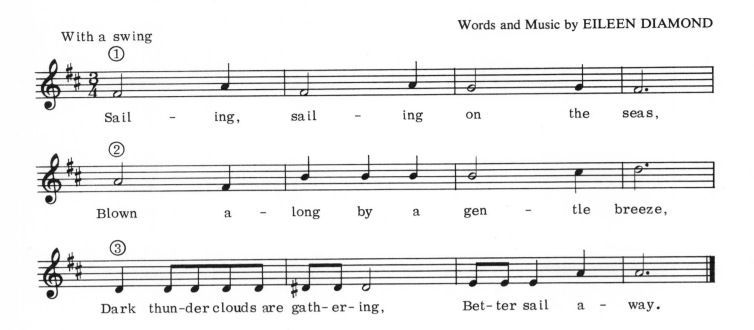

Sail - ing, sail - ing on the seas,

Blown a - long by a gen - tle breeze,

Dark thun-der clouds are gath-er-ing, Bet-ter sail a - way.

ACCOMPANIMENT OSTINATO

Sail - ing, sail a - way. - way.

ONLY TIME WILL TELL (3 parts)

Words and Music by EILEEN DIAMOND

Where did we come from? Where will we go?

What is our pur - pose here? Will we ev - er know?

On -ly time will tell. On - ly time will show.

ACCOMPANIMENT OSTINATO

On - ly time will show.

RAIN (3 parts)

Words and Music by EILEEN DIAMOND

ACCOMPANIMENT OSTINATO

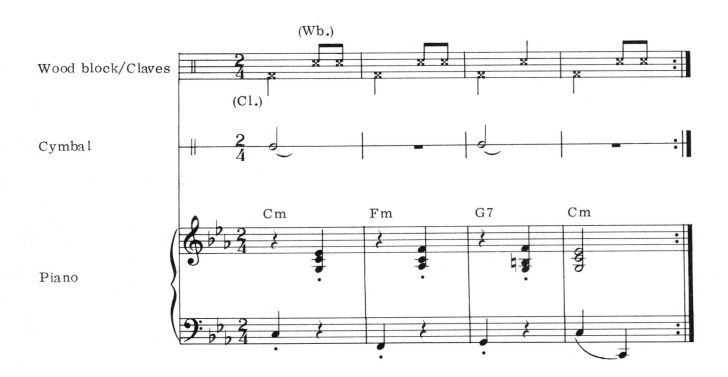

NOTE: Take extra care in practising the join between the first and second lines.

WHERE IS YOUR HOME? (3 parts)

Words and Music by EILEEN DIAMOND

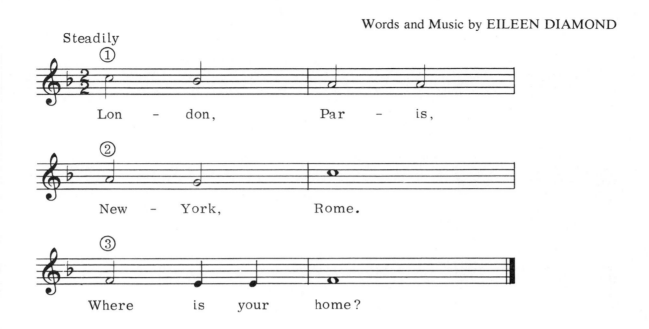

ACCOMPANIMENT OSTINATO

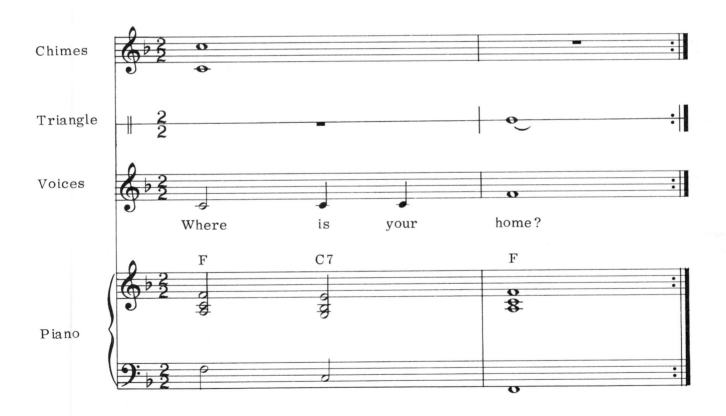

NOTE: Try varying the place names in the round — perhaps including some towns
in your area. Ask the class to suggest different places,
and encourage them to work out any new rhythms.

FLY AWAY (3 parts)

Words and Music by EILEEN DIAMOND

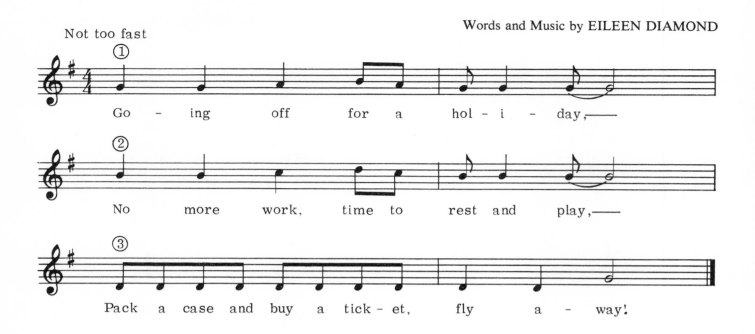

Not too fast

① Go - ing off for a hol - i - day, —

② No more work, time to rest and play, —

③ Pack a case and buy a tick - et, fly a - way!

ACCOMPANIMENT OSTINATO

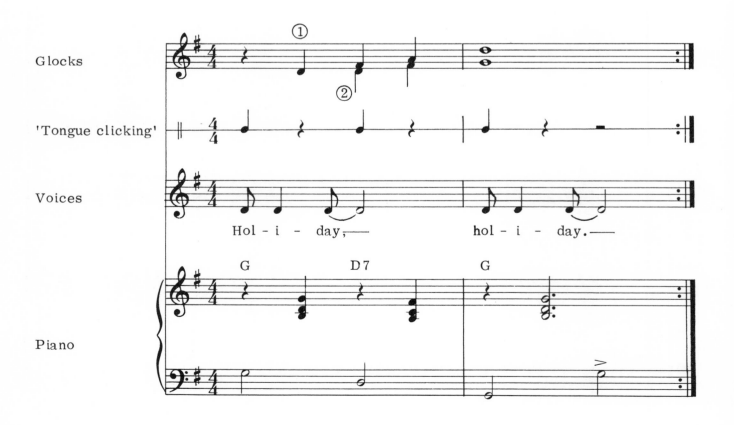

Glocks

'Tongue clicking'

Voices — Hol - i - day, — hol - i - day. —

Piano — G   D7   G

THE CRAZY ROUND (3 parts)

Words and Music by EILEEN DIAMOND

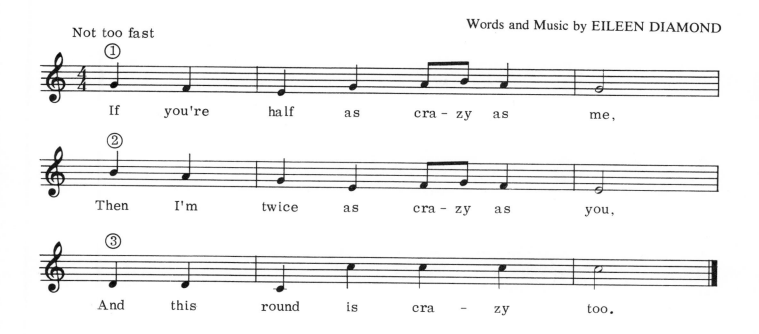

ACCOMPANIMENT OSTINATO

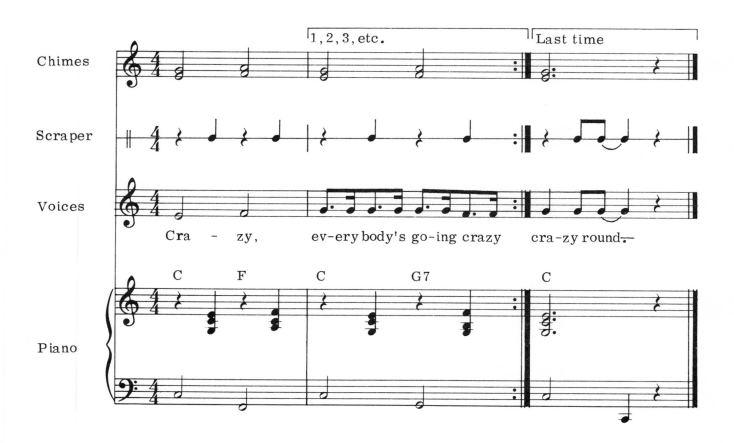

FOUR PART ROUNDS
FROST AND SNOW

Words and Music by EILEEN DIAMOND

ACCOMPANIMENT OSTINATO

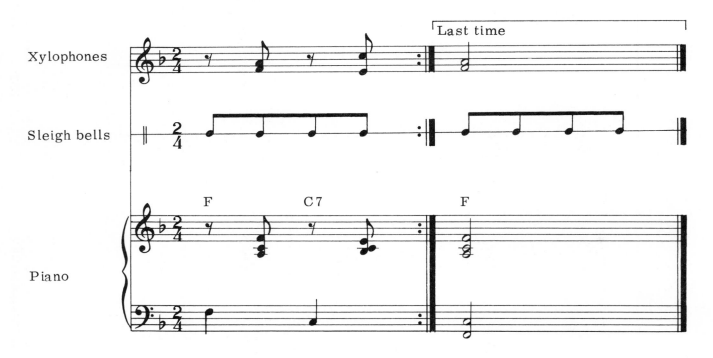

NOTE: Use two bars introduction, the **VOICES** entering on the second half of the second bar.

THE GARAGE ROUND (4 parts)

Words and Music by EILEEN DIAMOND

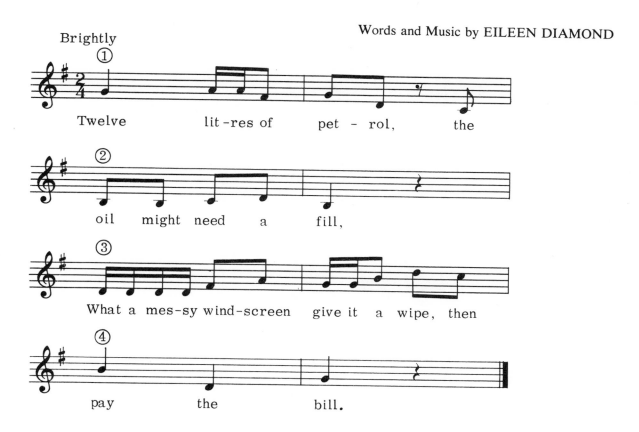

Brightly

① Twelve lit-res of pet-rol, the

② oil might need a fill,

③ What a mes-sy wind-screen give it a wipe, then

④ pay the bill.

ACCOMPANIMENT OSTINATO

Xylophones

Tambourine

Voices

Called at the garage one day, one day... Called at the garage one day!

Piano

THE BUSY ROUND (4 parts)

Words and Music by EILEEN DIAMOND

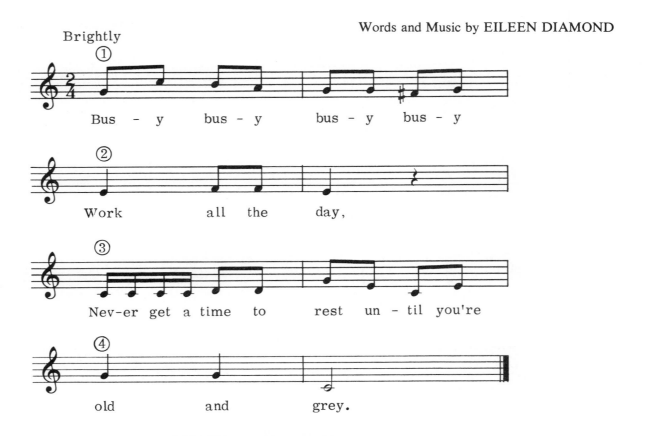

ACCOMPANIMENT OSTINATO

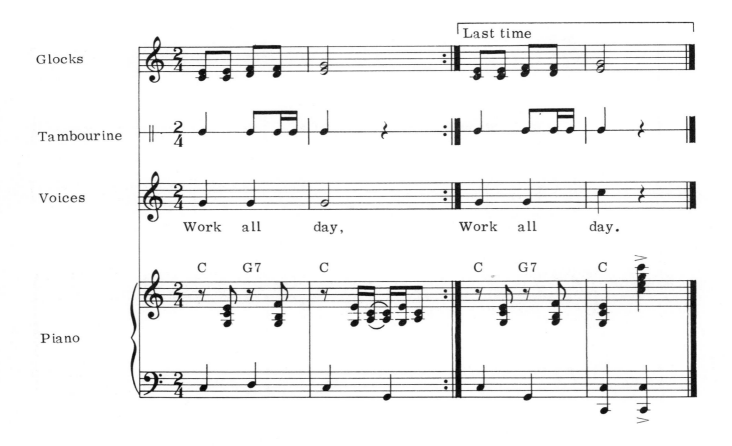

SHOPPING (4 parts)

Words and Music by EILEEN DIAMOND

Have to do my shop-ping in the su - per - mar - ket,

Salt and pep - per must - ard,

Six eggs and half a pound of cheese, And

don't for - get some nice fresh bread.

ACCOMPANIMENT OSTINATO

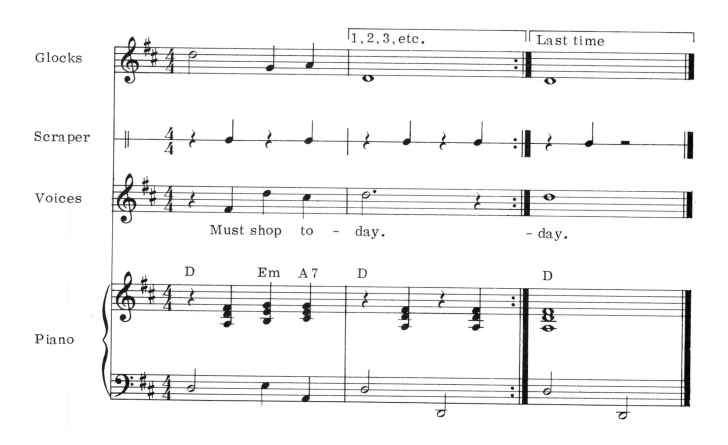

Must shop to - day. - day.

SING AWAY (4 parts)

Words and Music by EILEEN DIAMOND

ACCOMPANIMENT OSTINATO

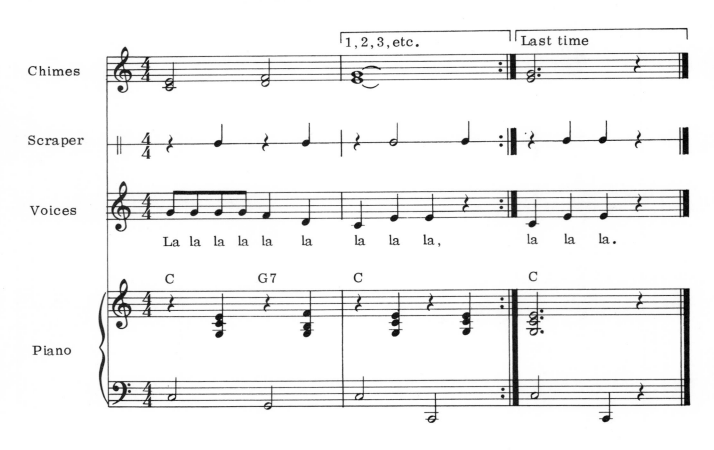

Printed by Halstan & Co. Ltd.,
Amersham, Bucks., England